WORLD GRAND PRIX

WGP RECOMMENDS

MOTOR CRUSH

CRUSH

Vol.1

Creators
BRENDEN FLETCHER
CAMERON STEWART
BABS TARR

Original Cover Artists
BABS TARR, CAMERON STEWART, LESLIE HUNG

Color & Production Assistant
HEATHER DANFORTH

Lettering
ADITYA BIDIKAR

Logo, Publication Design, WGP In-World Captions
TOM MULLER

Editor
JEANINE SCHAEFER

MOTOR CRUSH Vol. 1 · Originally published as MOTOR CRUSH #1-5

Special thanks to Nate Piekos & Blambot®

NOT A TAC, KIDDO. LAN, ON THE OTHER HAND...

LAN'S NEW. HE'LL LEARN.

BUT YOU GOTTA NIX THE SHOW-OFF. THIS IS A LEAGUE RACE.

...HOW YOU FEELING? EVERYTHING OKAY?

I'M FINE, DAD.

PROMISE.

FSSO

NOT A LOT OF MEAT LEFT ON THOSE BRAKE PADS, LAN.

NOT SURPRISED, THE WAY YOU CURVE. I'LL TAKE A LOOK WHEN WE GET BACK TO THE--

BZZT!!

COMPETITOR OH-ONE-ONE, *DOMINO SWIFT*, IDENTIFIED...

OH, NOT NOW...

INTERVIEW REQUEST INCOMING...

BIG RACE AHEAD! ANY WORDS FOR THE FANS?

DO I REALLY HAVE TO TALK TO THIS THING?

WE DID SIGN A CONTRACT, HON.

UNTIL YOU NET SOME PROPER SPONSORS, THE LIFE-STREAM RIGHTS ARE KEEPING US AFLOAT.

LAN'S BEEN VERY PATIENT WITH GETTING PAID...

BZZT! REPEAT QUERY--

WORDS FOR THE FANS?

tsk!

YEAH, YEAH, I'LL THINK OF SOME LATER.

LIFESTREAM

Domino Swift
Competitor 011

CATBALL, END
TRANSMISSION!

GO AWAY! OFF! SHOO!

World Grand Prix Media Channel

The World's Favorite Sport™

WORLDWIDE

Next WGP Circuit:
Nova Honda
Pop: 6,023,094

Famous Racers From Nova, Ranked

Visiting Nova?
Touch **HERE** For
Hotels & Nightlife

WORLD GRAND PRIX

HEAD2HEAD

DOMINO SWIFT

Win Probability: 7.8%

WGP RISING STAR

TRIVIA:
Daughter of former
WGP champ
Sullivan Swift

PLACE BET

DECIMUS WEXLER

Win Probability: 89%

TRIVIA:
Three-time cup
winner, *SPEED
MAGAZINE*'s
"Sexiest
Racer Alive"

PLACE BET

ON COURSE

Level: ADVANCED

Limited Straightaways, Tight Turns
Advantage: SWIFT

FINISH LINE

GAS NITRO REDUX DIESEL DURASTRON

WGP

MEMORIAL

Uri McLaren
TRIVIA: Deceased

Touch **HERE**
To Pay Respects

*WGP WARNING:
SAY NO TO ILLEGAL
ACCELERANTS!*

SAZERAC
TIRES

FLASHBACK

Touch **HERE**
To Replay
mclarencrash

GRAPHIC VIDEO

Uri was a good kid,
but scrammed up.

You could hear his engine from the stands. That rattle they make when they need another hit.

Uri knuckled. He knew he was gonna lose, so he overdosed his bike.

If we knew he was Crushing, figure the Race Patrol did too. It was only a matter of time until the League bounced him.

But anyone who uses Crush knows the risks.

You do what you gotta do to survive.

HEY KID, YOU--

DON'T YOU KNOCK?!

YOUR DAD WANTS YOU DOWN IN THE GARAGE.

...

Well, shit.

SONOYA'S GONNA CAP HER FIRST MEDIA STREAM!

WHAT?! YOU GOT INTO THE WGP?

I'M SO EXCITED, DOMINO! WE'RE FINALLY GONNA RACE TOGETHER!

COMPETITORS OH-ONE-ONE, OH-ONE-SEVEN, *DOMINO SWIFT, SONOYA VERMILION* IDENTIFIED...

OKAY, HOT TIP--THE CATBALLS ARE PESTS BUT THE WGP WANTS DRAMA, SO WE GOTTA PLAY IT UP. DEAL?

FRIENDLY RIVALRY? I'M SO IN!

LOOK WHAT THE CATBALL DRAGGED IN. WHAT BRINGS YOU TO TEAM SWIFT'S GARAGE? TRYING TO SPY ON YOUR COMPETITION?

DOMINO. YOU TAUGHT ME EVERYTHING I KNOW...AND I'M GONNA USE IT TO KICK YOUR BUTT AT THE RACE NEXT WEEK.

END MEDIA STREAM...

IN YOUR DREAMS, YA-YA.

I GOTTA STREAK. I'D SAY I'LL SEE YOU AT THE TRACK, BUT YOU'LL BE BEHIND ME...

HEY, WAIT! WE SHOULD CELEBRATE! CAKE AND FIZZ, LIKE OLD TIMES?

DAD.

IT'S CANNONBALL NIGHT.

Can't tell if it's engines revving or my stomach cranking me for not taking Dad up on that cake.

You know the biz is serious when I pass up a slice of Capixaba's Double Sweet.

If I'm caught racing for Crush, my career on the circuit is over. Team Swift is done. Dad's shop will close.

No big one, right? Just everything that matters to me on the line.

Like I haven't lost enough.

BACK FOR MORE, CRICKET?

REMEMBER, IF I WIN YOU PROMISED TO TELL ME YOUR NAME.

BUT YOU WON'T WIN, CALAX.

AND DON'T CALL ME THAT.

GOTTA CALL YOU **SOMETHING,** CRICKET.

GOOD LUCK OUT THERE.

HAH! SHE'LL NEED MORE THAN LUCK TO BEAT KING TYRE!

GOOD THING I'VE GOT THIS.

GRRR

So easy to shut him up.

But th
more
he can
from...

MORS EX MARIBUS
AKA MARI

GANG	GLADIATORS
SPECIALITY	CHAIN AND PAIN
CRUSH COUNT	0 WINS
TRIVIA	TALKS TRASH EASY CASH

HANNIBAL HOLOCAUST

GANG	MAGIC MONSTERS
SPECIALITY	THE HAMMERDROP
CRUSH COUNT	2 WINS
TRIVIA	FUZZY FACE DAMAGED MIND

KING TYRE

GANG	ROYAL BASTARD SQUAD
SPECIALITY	STICK A FORK IN IT
CRUSH COUNT	3 WINS
TRIVIA	ROLLS WITH THE DEVIL BOWS TO QUEEN CHRISTINE

DECORA

GANG	CLUB CLUB
SPECIALITY	CHAIN AND PAIN
CRUSH COUNT	3 WINS
TRIVIA	HARD CORE HAUTE COUTURE

CALAX GOTHARD
AKA SAVAGE

GANG	DENIM FANG
SPECIALITY	BEEFQUAKE
CRUSH COUNT	3.5 WINS
TRIVIA	TOUGH GUY ACT ACTUAL PUSSYCAT

And then there's me.

AKA CRICKET

GANG	NONE
SPECIALITY	BATTER UP
CRUSH COUNT	17 WINS
TRIVIA	HATES BEING CALLED CRICKET

Just one against every gang in Nova.

No sweat.

FUCK!

GROSS!

THIS GOES FOR THE REST OF YOU!

THE PRODUCERS WILL ONLY GIVE UNTIL YOU START TO TAKE.

YOU CHEAT, YOU STEAL... ...*YOU DIE!!*

COPS'LL BE HERE SOON. SOMEBODY GET A FUCKIN' MOP.

LOLA!

Nightmares.

Haven't had those since I was little.

What happened last night? I remember shooting a whole vial of Crush...and then...

How did I get home?

How did I escape?

All of my gear's here...what about the Crush?

Only two.

Real successful mission, Domino.

CRASH!

OH, IT'S YOU.

MORNING, KIDDO! RAN OUTTA COFFEE ON THE BOAT. JUST BREWING SOME UP BEFORE LAN GETS IN.

YOU, UH, EXPECTING *COMPANY?*

JUST EDGY. BAD DREAMS.

YOU KNOW I HATE THOSE NIGHT RACES. THEY GET YOU ALL CRANKED UP. YOU NEED TO RELAX.

WHEN LAN GETS HERE, WE'LL GO FOR *HUJOS*--

LAN'S DEAD.

WHAT?!

WHEN? WHAT HAPPENED?

PRODUCERS. THEY CAUGHT HIM TRYING TO JACK CRUSH AT CANNONBALL. THEY... *PUNISHED* HIM FOR IT.

IT WAS HORRIBLE.

AW, HELL. I KNEW THERE WAS SOMETHING OFF ABOUT HIM...

I TOLD YOU THESE GUYS ARE DANGEROUS. YOU'VE GOTTA HAVE ENOUGH CRUSH SAVED BY NOW, WE CAN FIND ANOTHER WAY--

LAN STOLE MY STASH TOO. IT'S ALMOST ALL GONE.

I'VE GOT NO CHOICE.

I CAN'T LET YOU GET YOURSELF KILLED...

DAD, I'M FINE.

I CAN HANDLE IT.

WHY WON'T YOU TELL ME WHERE I COME FROM?

GO AWAY.

WE'RE CLOSED.

HEY, LOLA.

DOMINO?!

WHAT ARE YOU DOING HERE? I THOUGHT I WAS CLEAR--

YOU WERE, BUT...

I DON'T WANT TO SEE YOU!

IT'S HARD ENOUGH WITH YOUR PICTURE ALL OVER THE WGP STREAMS--

That knife... my nightmare...

...IS EVERYTHING OKAY?

IT'S NOTHING.

ARE YOU IN TROUBLE? DO YOU NEED HELP?

STOP IT, DOM!

SMAK!!

IT'S NONE OF YOUR BUSINESS!

LOOK, I KNOW I DROVE YOU AWAY. I NEVER SHOULD HAVE LIED TO YOU.

BUT MAYBE WE CAN HELP EACH OTHER. YOU'RE THE BEST MECHANIC IN NOVA--

...OH.

YOU'RE HERE FOR A BIKE.

OF COURSE YOU ARE.

...WHAT HAPPENED TO THE ONE I GAVE YOU?

IT'S...IT'S GONE. I LOST IT.

I NEED TO RUN THE CANNONBALL AGAIN AND--

SMASH!!

FUCKING CANNONBALL.

YOU KNOW, FOR A SECOND I THOUGHT YOU'D CHANGED.

BUT IT'S IN YOUR BONES, ISN'T IT?

THIS WAS A MISTAKE.

I'LL GO.

I KNOW YOU DON'T HAVE ANY REASON TO TRUST ME.

BUT IF YOU NEED ME, I'LL BE THERE FOR YOU.

OPEN

JUST STICK TO RACING, DOMINO.

IT'S WHAT YOU'RE GOOD AT.

WORLD GRAND PRIX

WGP

INFOPOP

11:52 BZ
87°V / SUNNY

COUNTDOWN TO RACE:
6:06:22:05

Touch **HERE** for media updates

I promised I'd walk out of that bar for good.

But that weird nightmare kept itching at the back of my mind.

It didn't feel like a dream anymore, but a **vision**.

I had to see if it was true.

And if it is, those goons should be showing up any time now--

...Shit.

I don't know if I'm relieved or even more freaked out.

TIME'S UP, LADY. WE WARNED YOU.

NOW WE GOTTA HURT YOU.

PLEASE, NO...!

LEAVE HER ALONE.

THEY'LL BE HERE SOON.

I CAN MAYBE REROUTE THE CIRCUITRY OF THE DISC TO SUPERCHARGE OUR BIKE. BUT THAT DEPENDS ON WHETHER THE POWER CELLS--

JUST DO IT!

I'LL TRY TO KEEP THEM BUSY.

FZZK

I CAN HEAR THEM!

THEY'RE CLOSE!

VRRrrm

RRKM

TEN SECONDS, LO!

COME ON...COME ON!

HERE THEY COME!!

VRRT

!

SKRKK

SKRKK

WHAT DID YOU DO?

I REVERSED THE REMOTE FUNCTIONALITY OF THE DISC AND SENT A SIGNAL TO LOCK THEIR WHEELS...

PRETTY SIMPLE.

EERGH...

YOU GENIUS, I LOVE YOU!

I MEAN... UH...YOU KNOW...

WE SHOULD GO.

WGP ALERT

MAX
SPEED

20 40 60 80 100 120 140 160 180

A   WARNING   MPH   ⚠

POWER   FUEL   C   **185**   H +

TEN MINUTES.

JUST ENOUGH TIME FOR A CUP OF TEA.

...SO MY DAD MISSES YOU, AND I KNOW YOU MISS *HIM,* AND FOR THAT ALONE WE SHOULD TRY TO WORK TOGETHER.

SURE, DOM. AND THIS HAS NOTHING TO DO WITH COVERING YOUR OWN ASS.

MY DEAL WITH THE PRODUCERS IS MY DEAL. YES, IF I LOSE THEN THEY COME FOR ME. THEY'LL OWN ME AND THE SHOP AND DAD WILL DIE OF A BROKEN HEART.

I CAN DO IT. YOU KNOW I CAN.

BUT I NEED YOU TO HELP ME PULL IT OFF.

NO LIES THIS TIME. NO SECRETS.

I PROMISE.

WAIT A MINUTE...

LOLA?

OH MY GOD, YOU'RE BACK?!

WOULDN'T BE A TEAM WITHOUT HER...

HI, SONOYA!! GOOD TO SEE YOU AGAIN!

AW, YOU TWO ARE THE CUTEST! I'M SO HAPPY YOU'RE BACK TOGETHER!

WELL, NOT EXACTLY...

WE'LL CATCH UP LATER, LOLA! GOTTA GET TO MY BIKE BEFORE I LOSE SIGHT OF MY MAN-CANDY!

GOOD LUCK, DOM!

WE'RE UP IN THREE.

YOU READY, KIDDO?

REMEMBER TO KEEP YOUR CHEST DOWN HARD ON THE TANK FOR THIS ONE.

YOUR FRONT TIRE NEEDS AS MUCH BITE AS SHE CAN GET...

WGP WARNING: SAY NO TO ILLEGAL ACCELERANTS!

MAD Agency—
TESTING IN PROGRESS

MACHINE ANTI DOPING

MAD

...only this isn't one I'm looking forward to having.

I SHOULD BE BACK IN A FEW HOURS. JUST GOTTA DELIVER THIS OLD GIRL TO HER RIGHTFUL OWNER AND PICK UP LOLA'S ORDER IN TOWN.

I NEED TO TALK TO YOU.

SURE. WHAT'S UP?

SOMETHING HAPPENED LAST NIGHT. SOMETHING **IMPORTANT**.

HAVE YOU EVER SEEN THIS SYMBOL BEFORE?

WHERE DID YOU GET THIS?

YOU **HAVE** SEEN IT BEFORE. YOU KNOW WHAT IT IS, DON'T YOU?

WHAT ELSE DO YOU KNOW? WHO GAVE IT TO ME? IS HE LIKE ME?

GET RID OF IT.

WHAT? **NO!** THIS IS A CLUE TO WHO I REALLY AM!

HE SAID I'M SUPPOSED TO **DO** SOMETHING, I'M SUPPOSED TO BE **MORE**--

DAD? **DAD!**

NOW YOU LISTEN TO ME. FORGET THIS.

I HAVE NEVER BEEN MORE SERIOUS. **DROP IT.**

DAD, PLEASE! THIS IS DRIVING ME CRAZY, DON'T YOU GET THAT?

THIS IS TOO **DANGEROUS,** DOM. DO YOU GET **THAT?**

THIS ISN'T THE WGP, IT'S NOT THE CANNONBALL. THIS IS LIFE AND DEATH. YOURS AND MINE AND--

I'M YOUR FATHER AND I'M TELLING YOU TO DROP IT.

SLAM!

BUT YOU'RE NOT MY FATHER!

SKRKK

And I've never felt less like his daughter.

WHAT ARE YOU DOING? IS THIS YOUR DAD'S STUFF? THESE ARE PAPERS GOING BACK--

NONE OF YOUR BUSINESS, OKAY?

IT'S PERSONAL.

...OH.

I'LL... UH...I'LL LEAVE YOU ALONE.

...I'M ADOPTED.

WHAT?

I'VE KNOWN SINCE I WAS A KID.

BUT I DON'T KNOW WHERE I'M FROM. I KEEP ASKING, BUT DAD WON'T TELL ME.

THOUGHT I COULD FIND A CLUE IN HIS STUFF.

WHY DIDN'T YOU EVER TELL ME?

DAD DIDN'T WANT ANYONE TO KNOW.

HE'S VERY... PROTECTIVE.

DOM, IF THERE'S ANYTHING I CAN DO...I'M HERE.

THANKS, LO.

BUT I CAN HANDLE THIS.

WHAT?

YOU'RE DOING IT AGAIN.

YOU'RE SO STUBBORN, DOM.

EVERY INCH OF ME TOLD ME TO STAY AWAY FROM YOU, BUT HERE I AM ANYWAY. I KEEP HOPING THAT YOU'LL PROVE ME WRONG, THAT YOU'LL FINALLY SEE THAT ALL I'M TRYING TO DO IS CARE FOR YOU. BUT YOU JUST KEEP THAT DOOR TO YOUR HEART CLOSED.

WHY WON'T YOU LET ME IN?

FOR THE LAST FEW DAYS YOU'VE WANTED NOTHING TO DO WITH ME!

NOW YOU WANT IN?

DOM...

...I *ALWAYS* WANTED IN.

Dammit.

*If I do find out who I really am, maybe I won't be such an **ass**.*

I gotta get out and clear my head.

YOU'RE GONNA LEARN A LESSON, FINGERS...

He's here.

I thought he might have been trying to help me.

But he's just standing there, watching.

What is this, a **game?** You're just gonna fuck with my head and watch me squirm?

Well, **fuck you,** too! I'll--

What...?

...THE **HELL** IS THAT...?

VNNNNN NNN NNNN

"I'LL NEVER FORGET THAT...THING."

=SNF=

SHH... SHHH...

VNNNN VNNNN

PLEASE, BABYGIRL, PLEASE DON'T CRY...

"I'VE ALWAYS BEEN GOOD AT THE WHEEL BUT THAT NIGHT MY HANDS WOULDN'T STOP TREMBLING.

"I PUSHED MY VAN TO THE BREAKING POINT...

"I BARELY MADE IT BACK TO THE SHOP BEFORE THE NEXT PROBLEM HIT."

SAGE!

DAD!

THE CHAIN THAT BINDS HIM IS ANCHORED UNDER MY WHEEL.

IF THAT BIKE MOVES, SULLIVAN SWIFT WILL FALL TO THE SEA BELOW.

AND IT *WILL* MOVE.

BUT YOU CAN SAVE HIM, DOMINO. I'M GIVING YOU A CHANCE.

IF YOU'RE FAST ENOUGH.

CRUSH

CRU

CRU

WORLD
GRAND
PRIX

WORLD
GRAND
PRIX

WGP
RECOMMENDS

MOTOR MOTOR

CRUSH

CRUSH

RISING STAR

CRUSH

CRU

CRU

INFOPOP
EXHIBITION

WGP

ORIGINAL MOTOR CRUSH #1–5
COVERS, ILLUSTRATED BY BABS TARR
AND CAMERON STEWART, DESIGNED
BY TOM MULLER.

SAY HELLO TO BRENDEN!
WGP RISING STAR

BRENDEN FLETCHER
@BRENDENFLETCHER

Brenden Fletcher is a writer known for his work on DC Comics series *Gotham Academy*, *Black Canary* and the *New York Times* bestselling *Batgirl of Burnside* with Cameron and Babs.

He contributed the acclaimed *Flash* story to the Eisner and Harvey Award-winning *Wednesday Comics* series and has created comics for brands including *Mighty Morphin' Power Rangers*, *Assassin's Creed*, *Attack On Titan,* and Adult Swim. He lives in Brooklyn, NY with his partner and two cats.

SAY HELLO TO BABS!
WGP RISING STAR

BABS TARR
@BABSDRAWS

Babs Tarr is a graduate of the illustration program at the Maryland Institute College of Art. Before entering comics, she worked in a variety of fields including mobile gaming, toy design, and editorial illustrations.

Spotted online for her personal illustration work, she was invited to join Brenden and Cameron on the *Batgirl of Burnside* revamp for DC Comics and immediately became one of the most distinctive and popular new artists in comics. She currently lives in Charleston, South Carolina.

SAY HELLO TO CAMERON!
WGP RISING STAR

CAMERON STEWART
@CAMERONMSTEWART

Cameron Stewart is a writer and artist best known for his work with Brenden and Babs on DC's *Batgirl of Burnside*, as well as the illustrator of *Fight Club 2*, both *New York Times* bestsellers. His original graphic novel *Sin Titulo* won Eisner and Shuster Awards, and was nominated for Eagle, Harvey, and Stoker Awards.

He has written and/or illustrated a variety of comics, including *Assassin's Creed*, *Batman and Robin*, *BPRD*, *The Other Side,* and many more. Having lived in London, Birmingham, Montreal, Berlin and Glasgow, he has finally settled in his hometown of Toronto...for now.

SAY HELLO TO ADITYA!
WGP RISING STAR

ADITYA BIDIKAR
@ADITYAB

Aditya Bidikar is currently lettering *Drifter*, *Black Cloud*, and *Winnebago Graveyard* for Image Comics, *Night's Dominion* for Oni Press, Grant Morrison's *18 Days* and *Avatarex* for Graphic India, and the *Femme Magnifique* anthology, among others. In a previous life, he's been a comics editor, and has written short stories for the *Faction Paradox* and *Iris Wildthyme* series of prose anthologies.

He lives and works out of Pune, India.

SAY HELLO TO TOM!
WGP RISING STAR

TOM MULLER
@HELLOMULLER

Tom Muller has been designing comics for over 15 years and picked up the odd Eisner and Harvey Awards nomination along the way. He's best known for his design and art-direction on *Zero*, *Wolf*, *Drifter*, *Material*, *Snowfall*, and *The Violent* at Image; his logos for DC Comics' *Suicide Squad*, *Unfollow*, *Survivors' Club*, and *Trillium*; and his design and cover art for Valiant's *Divinity* series, *Ninjak*, *X-O Manowar*, *Bloodshot*, and *Book of Death*. Originally from Belgium, he lives in London with his wife and two cats.

SAY HELLO TO JEANINE!
WGP RISING STAR

JEANINE SCHAEFER
@J9SCHAEFER

Jeanine Schaefer has been editing comics for over ten years. Titles include Marvel Comics' *X-Men*, *She-Hulk*, and the Eisner-nominated *Young Adult Mystic*, *Jonesy* at BOOM!, and the upcoming *Prima* from Image Comics. She also founded *Girl Comics*, an anthology celebrating the history of women at Marvel.

She lives in Los Angeles with her husband and two children, and sporadically runs a Tumblr celebrating the special relationship between nerds and cats.

June 2017. Published by Image Comics, Inc. Office of publication: 2701 NW Vaughn St., Ste. 780, Portland, OR 97210. Copyright © 2017 BRENDEN FLETCHER, CAMERON STEWART and BARBARA TARR. All rights reserved. MOTOR CRUSH™ (including all prominent characters featured herein), its logo and all character likenesses are trademarks of Brenden Fletcher, Cameron Stewart and Barbara Tarr, unless otherwise noted. Image Comics® and its logos are registered trademarks of Image Comics, Inc. No part of this publication may be reproduced or transmitted, in any form or by any means (except short excerpts for review purposes) without express written permission of Image Comics, Inc. All names, characters, events and locales in this publication are entirely fictional. Any resemblance to actual living persons (living or dead), events or places, without satiric intent, is coincidental. Printed in the U.S.A. For information regarding the CPSIA on this printed material call: 203-595-3636 and provide reference # RICH - 736492. For international rights, contact: foreignlicensing@imagecomics.com. ISBN: 978-1-5343-0189-4 Barnes & Noble ISBN: 978-1-5343-0389-8 Kinokuniya ISBN: 978-1-5343-0399-7 Newbury ISBN: 978-1-5343-0411-6 DCBS ISBN: 978-1-5343-0412-3 Forbidden Planet / Big Bang IBSN: 978-1-5343-0413-0 Heroes ISBN: 978-1-5343-0414-7 Big B ISBN: 978-1-5343-0415-4

IMAGECOMICS, INC

Robert Kirkman: Chief Operating Officer / Erik Larsen: Chief Financial Officer / Todd McFarlane: President / Marc Silvestri: Chief Executive Officer / Jim Valentino: Vice-President / Eric Stephenson: Publisher / Corey Murphy: Director of Sales / Jeff Boison: Director of Publishing Planning & Book Trade Sales / Chris Ross: Director of Digital Sales / Jeff Stang: Director of Specialty Sales / Kat Salazar: Director of PR & Marketing / Branwyn Bigglestone: Controller / Sue Korpela: Accounts Manager / Drew Gill: Art Director / Brett Warnock: Production Manager / Meredith Wallace: Print Manager / Tricia Ramos: Traffic Manager / Briah Skelly: Publicist / Aly Hoffman: Conventions & Events Coordinator / Sasha Head: Sales & Marketing Production Designer / David Brothers: Branding Manager / Melissa Gifford: Content Manager / Drew Fitzgerald: Publicity Assistant / Vincent Kukua: Production Artist / Erika Schnatz: Production Artist / Ryan Brewer: Production Artist / Shanna Matuszak: Production Artist / Carey Hall: Production Artist / / Esther Kim: Direct Market Sales Representative / Emilio Bautista: Digital Sales Representative/ Leanna Caunter: Accounting Assistant / Chloe Ramos-Peterson: Library Market Sales Representative / Marla Eizik: Administrative Assistant /